Park
Shark

By Jenny Moore

Illustrated by
Daniel Limon

"In we go, ducklings," quacks Mum.

"We will go for a moonlight dip."

"Oh no!" quacks Doris.

"I can see a shark!"

"A shark?" quacks Mum.

"It is a shark," quacks Dee.

"I can see a sharp fin."

"It will get us!" quack the ducklings.

"I bet it has sharp teeth,"
quacks Dennis.

Mum pops into the pond.

She swims...

"Aaah! It is a shark!" she quacks.

"I can see the fin too."

25

"No," quack the ducklings.

"It was a boat sail all along!"

Quiz

1. Who sees the 'shark' first?
a) Doris
b) Mum
c) Dee

2. What does Mum say about the 'shark'?
a) "It's a big, fat shark!"
b) "I bet it has sharp teeth!"
c) "No sharks are in the park!"

3. What do the ducklings see?
a) Big teeth
b) A long tail
c) A sharp fin

4. What helps the ducks?

a) The sun

b) The moon

c) The frog

5. What is the 'shark'?

a) A frog

b) A big fish

c) A sail boat

Turn over for answers

Book Bands for Guided Reading

The Institute of Education book banding system is a scale of colours that reflects the various levels of reading difficulty. The bands are assigned by taking into account the content, the language style, the layout and phonics. Word, phrase and sentence level work is also taken into consideration.

Maverick Early Readers are a bright, attractive range of books covering the pink to white bands. All of these books have been book banded for guided reading to the industry standard and edited by a leading educational consultant.

To view the whole Maverick Readers scheme, visit our website at www.maverickearlyreaders.com

Or scan the QR code above to view our scheme instantly!

Quiz Answers: 1a, 2c, 3c, 4a, 5c

Park
Shark

Maverick

Early Readers

'Park Shark'
An original concept by Jenny Moore
© Jenny Moore

Illustrated by Daniel Limon

Published by MAVERICK ARTS PUBLISHING LTD
Studio 11, City Business Centre, 6 Brighton Road,
Horsham, West Sussex, RH13 5BB
© Maverick Arts Publishing Limited August 2021
+44 (0)1403 256941

A CIP catalogue record for this book is available at the British Library.

ISBN 978-1-84886-812-0

www.maverickbooks.co.uk

This book is rated as: Yellow Band (Guided Reading)
It follows the requirements for Phase 3 phonics.
Most words are decodable, and any non-decodable words are familiar,
supported by the context and/or represented in the artwork.